CATS WITH HANDS

BY

JOE MARTIN

First Printing December 2006

ISBN: 0-9745967-2-8

ISBN13: 978-0-9745967-2-3

Neatly Chiseled Features
N1870 Loramoor Drive
Lake Geneva, WI. 53147
262-248-9460-phone
262-248-3431-fax
mrboffo@mrboffo.com-email
cats@catswithhands.com-email

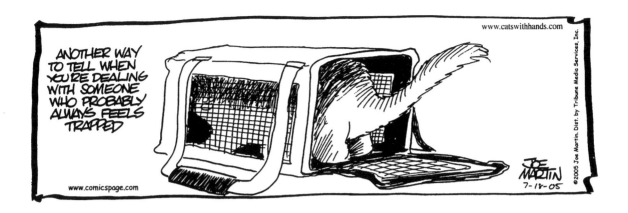

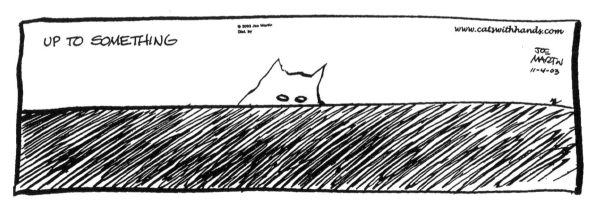

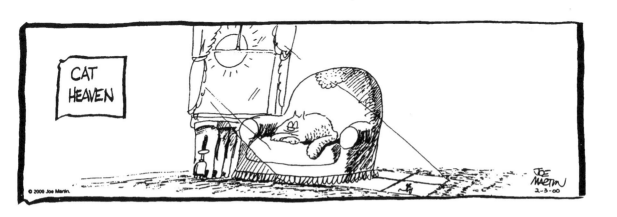

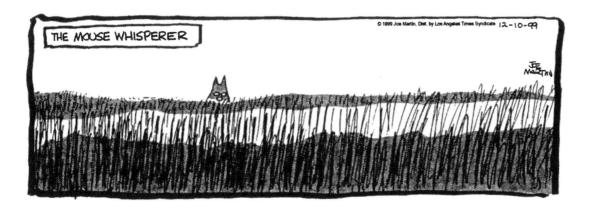

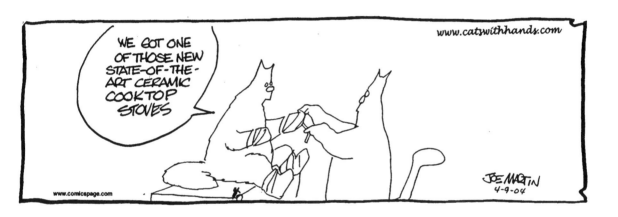

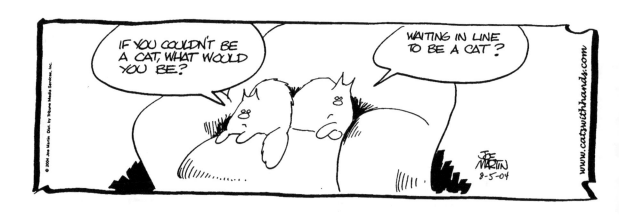

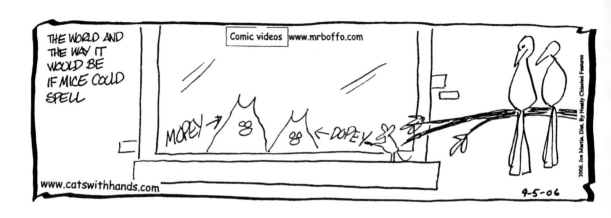

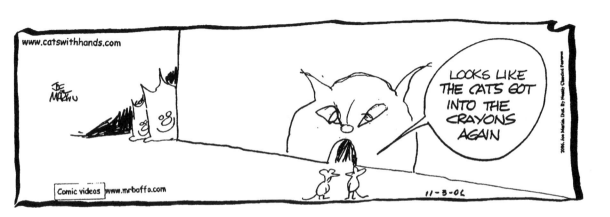

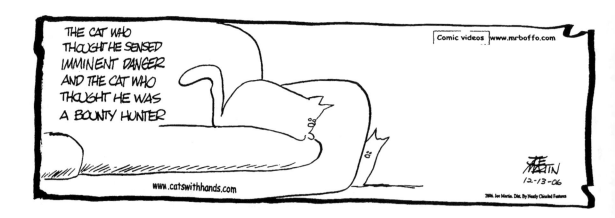

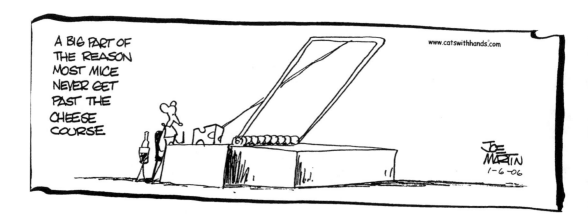

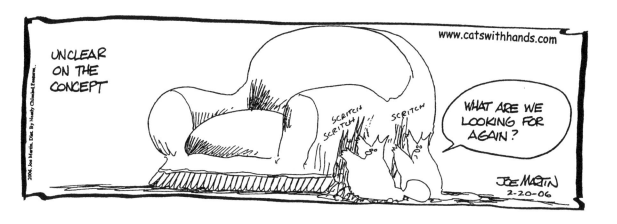

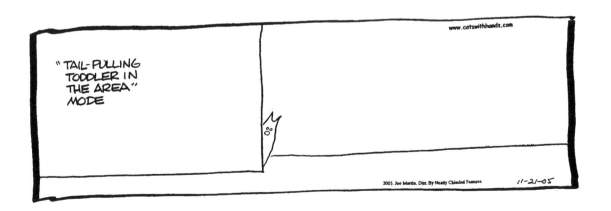

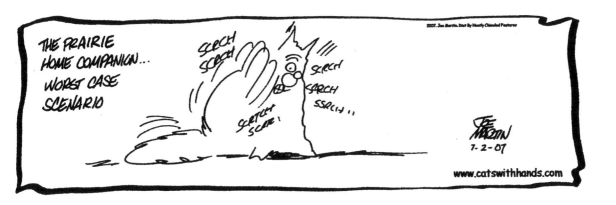

Made in the USA